My Spelling Workbook

Prim-Ed
Publishing

Prim-Ed Publishing would like to thank the teachers and pupils from the following schools for their assistance in the production of this *My Spelling Workbook* programme:

Merrylee Primary School, Glasgow

Balbardie Primary School, West Lothian

Brackens Primary School, Dundee

Braehead Primary School, Dumbarton

East Fulton Primary School, Renfrewshire

Knockburn Primary School, Glasgow

Pitfour Primary School, Aberdeenshire

Saracen Primary School, Glasgow

St. Catherine's Primary School, Glasgow

The Mary Russell School, Renfrewshire

Woodlands Primary School, Renfrewshire

My Spelling Workbook – Book F
© Prim-Ed Publishing

Offices in: United Kingdom: PO Box 2840, Coventry, CV6 5ZY
Australia: PO Box 332, Greenwood, Western Australia 6924
Republic of Ireland: Bosheen, New Ross, Co. Wexford, Ireland

Published in 2003 Prim-Ed Publishing
ISBN 1 86400 766 4

Introduction

Welcome to *My Spelling Workbook*. This book has lots of different activities to help you improve your spelling. Here are some tips to show you the best way to use your book.

- **Learning Words**

  Each list of words in the book has two practise columns to write the words. There is also a column for your teacher to tick if you get your dictation correct. Any words which you spell wrongly can be added to the 'Difficult Words I Have Found' table. You can also add any other difficult words you find.

- **Look, Say, Cover, Write, Check**

  These words are to remind you of the best way to learn to spell. You should follow this when you are learning each word. Use the flap to cover the list words when you practise them.

- **Recording your Scores**

  At the back of the book, you will find a grid for recording your scores for each unit. This will help you to keep track of how you are improving with your spelling.

- **How to Become a Better Speller**

  1. *Have a go!*
     Write the word on the piece of paper.
     Does it look right? If it doesn't look right, try writing it another way.

  2. *Look around your classroom*
     There are probably many words around you that you just didn't notice.

  3. *Use a dictionary*
     Try using a dictionary before you ask a teacher.

  4. *Ask the teacher*
     If you have tried the first three, then ask a teacher for help.

Contents

Revision Unit 1

List Words	Practise	Practise	D
because			
going			
laugh			
paper			
goes			
today			
it's			
something			
sing			
country			

All Mixed Up

1. Unjumble these revision words.

   (a) lahug   _____   (b) subcaee   _____

   (c) tunyorc   _____   (d) tinmegsho   _____

   (e) yatod   _____   (f) noggi   _____

Missing Words

2. Complete using the revision words.

   (a) He is _____ to the shop _____ we need milk.

   (b) _____ a fine day _____.

   (c) Can you _____ some _____ music?

   (d) Say _____ funny to make him _____.

Shape Sorter

3. Write a revision word that fits in each shape.

   (a) 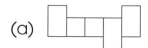   (b)

   (c) 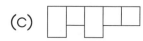   (d)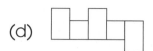

4. Find 12 mistakes and write them correctly on the lines.

Can you write down the words to that county music on this piece of

_____

papper Its sumthing I am goin to sang todday at the consert. I don't

_____

want anyone to lagh at me becase I forget how it gose!

_____

Word Hunt

5. (a) Which three words are compound words?   _____

_____

_____

(b) Which word is a contraction?   _____

(c) Two words come from the same verb.
What is the verb?   _____

(d) Which two words rhyme with thing?   _____

_____

Alphabetical Order

6. Write all the revision words in alphabetical order.

_____

_____

_____

_____

Mixed Up Sentences

7. Unjumble the sentences and write them below.

(a) to country at show. I sing talent am song a going the

_____

(b) had laugh We a joke was funny. the good because so

_____

(c) going holiday a country. on Today, are to we different

_____

List Words	Practise	Practise	D
area			
agenda			
paella			
umbrella			
hero			
zero			
piano			
tomato			
until			
diamond			

Mirror Writing

1. Write the mirror written words correctly.

   (a) diamond

   (b) tomato

   (c) paella

   (d) agenda

   (e) piano

   (f) area

Revision Words

mansion

river

minimum

inspect

cassette

magical

Letters into Words

2. Write three list words using the letters on the umbrella.

_____

_____

_____

Jumbled Words

3. Two words are jumbled together. Write the two words.

   (a) aeroplahel

   (b) todtomnamidoa

   _____

   _____

   _____

   _____

Difficult words I have found	Practise	Practise

4. Use list and revision words to solve the crossword.

Across

1. It keeps the rain off.
3. Bigger than a stream.
5. The least possible.
9. It has ivory keys.
11. Tape.
13. Programme.
14. Nil.

Down

1. Till such time as.
2. The man of the moment.
4. Examine closely.
5. Enchanted.
6. A very large house.

7. A Spanish dish.
8. Red food used in salads.
10. Region.
12. Valuable jewel.

Secret Code

5. Use the secret code to find out the list or revision word.

a	c	e	g	i	l	m	n	o	p	s	t
1	2	3	4	5	6	7	8	9	10	11	12

(a) _ _ _ _ _ _ _ _
    7 1 8 11 5 9 8

(b) _ _ _ _ _ _ _
    5 8 11 10 3 2 12

(c) _ _ _ _ _ _ _
    7 1 4 5 2 1 6

(d) _ _ _ _ _ _
    10 1 3 6 6 1

(e) _ _ _ _ _
    10 5 1 8 9

Mixed Up Sentences

6. Unjumble the sentences and write them below.

(a) did the be such demand. The paella not chef realise would in

_____

(b) came inspect the the The agenda to meeting. boss for

_____

List Words	Practise	Practise	D
taxi			
spaghetti			
macaroni			
graffiti			
emu			
menu			
Peru			
haiku			
side			
necessary			

Alphabetical Order

1. Write these words in alphabetical order.

   spaghetti   menu

   macaroni   side

   (a) _____

   (b) _____

   (c) _____

   (d) _____

Incorrect Words

2. (a) grafiti _____

   (b) macaruny _____

   (c) hiku _____

   (d) nesessary _____

   (e) spagetti _____

Revision Words		
civil	memory	occasion
flavour	miniature	inspector

All Mixed Up

3. Unjumble these list words.

   (a) senraysec _____   (b) naimorac _____

   (c) traifgif _____   (d) nuem _____

   (e) dies _____   (f) akuhi _____

Difficult words I have found	Practise	Practise

4. Use list and revision words to solve the wordsearch.

spaghetti	menu
graffiti	emu
macaroni	Peru
taxi	haiku
side	necessary
civil	memory
occasion	flavour
miniature	inspector

n	g	f	b	v	n	s	n	m	u	d	l	m
o	e	d	n	c	i	v	i	l	f	m	p	e
i	h	c	m	d	m	b	b	l	g	e	e	m
s	j	i	e	c	l	v	v	k	r	n	o	o
a	k	n	n	s	k	s	c	u	u	u	i	r
c	l	o	b	x	s	p	t	r	o	s	u	y
c	p	r	v	z	j	a	x	e	v	a	y	m
o	o	a	c	a	i	g	r	P	a	g	t	k
q	i	c	k	n	h	h	z	y	l	w	i	o
w	u	a	i	s	g	e	x	j	f	e	x	i
e	y	m	z	d	f	t	c	u	k	i	a	h
i	n	s	p	e	c	t	o	r	h	r	t	j
r	t	s	a	i	t	i	f	f	a	r	g	n

Memory Master

5. (a) Cover the list and revision words. Write three from memory.

_____   _____   _____

(b) For each word, write a question that has the word as its answer.

(i) _____

(ii) _____

(iii) _____

My Meanings

6. Write a definition for each of the list and revision words below. Use a dictionary to check your answers.

(a) flavour_____

_____

_____

(b) graffiti_____

_____

(c) miniature _____

(d) civil _____

List Words	Practise	Practise	D
authority			
display			
enemy			
holiday			
lady			
gateway			
baby			
key			
conscience			
milk			

Plurals

1. Choose 's' or 'ies' to make plural nouns.

Singular	Plural
(a) lady	_____
(b) holiday	_____
(c) enemy	_____
(d) key	_____

Revision Words	
darling	struggle
section	towel
decision	selection

Synonyms

3. Find a list word with a similar meaning.

(a) foe _____

(b) vacation _____

(c) infant _____

(d) show _____

(e) entrance _____

Missing Letters

2. Complete the list word.

(a) __ __ __ __ __ i e __ __ e

(b) __ __ __ e __ a __

(c) __ __ __ __ o __ i __ __

(d) __ o __ i __ a __

Difficult words I have found	Practise	Practise

4. Use list and revision words to solve the crossword.

Across

1. A female with a title.
6. A piece of something.
7. A baby drinks this.
9. Put on a show.
11. Power.
12. It fits in a lock.
14. Entrance.
16. The part chosen.

Down

2. Verdict.
3. Foe.
4. Sense of right and wrong.
5. Time when there is no school.
8. A newborn.
10. Wrestle.
13. Sweetheart.
15. Cloth to dry in.

Word Worm

milkstruggleholidayselectiongatewaykeytowelladybabysection

5. Circle the words in the word worm. Write the six words which are not in the word worm.

_____ _____

_____ _____

_____ _____

Missing Words

6. Use list or revision words to complete these sentences.

(a) Remember to take a _____ on _____ with you.

(b) It was a _____ for the _____ to enter the fortress.

(c) Those in _____ _____ the rules on the board.

(d) It will be on my _____ if I make the wrong

_____ .

List Words	Practise	Practise	D
mouse			
die			
woman			
tooth			
sheep			
scissors			
child			
foot			
fulfil			
money			

Small Words

1. Write a list word that contains these small words.

   (a) one _____

   (b) is _____

   (c) use _____

   (d) an _____

   (e) he _____

Compound Words

2. Add a list word to make a compound word.

   (a) _____ball

   (b) _____dog

   (c) _____hood

   (d) _____trap

   (e) _____brush

Rhyming Words

3. Choose a rhyming word from the list.

   (a) leap _____

   (b) spy _____

   (c) until _____

   (d) sunny _____

Revision Words

microphone	spectacular
weakling	attract
function	poultry

Difficult words I have found	Practise	Practise

4. Use list and revision words to solve the wordsearch.

mouse	die
woman	tooth
sheep	scissors
child	foot
fulfil	money
microphone	spectacular
weakling	attract
function	poultry

s	h	e	e	p	h	j	q	a	n	h	k	t
q	p	f	m	o	u	s	e	z	b	y	m	o
w	g	e	i	n	o	i	t	c	n	u	f	o
e	h	d	c	m	g	k	w	x	g	u	o	t
t	c	a	r	t	t	a	e	s	g	s	o	h
r	j	s	o	n	a	d	r	n	t	c	t	i
t	k	a	p	b	f	c	i	w	r	i	m	o
l	l	z	h	v	d	l	u	e	f	s	o	l
i	p	x	o	c	k	l	t	l	v	s	n	p
f	o	c	n	a	s	p	y	e	a	o	e	h
l	i	v	e	x	p	o	u	l	t	r	y	d
u	u	w	o	m	a	n	u	d	c	s	j	f
f	y	b	n	z	a	o	i	c	h	i	l	d

Plurals

5. Write down the plural of these nouns.

(a) foot _____   (b) money _____

(c) tooth _____   (d) mouse _____

(e) woman _____   (f) sheep _____

(g) scissors _____   (h) child _____

(i) weakling _____   (j) poultry _____

Extend Yourself

6. (a) Use a dictionary to find two meanings for this word.

mouse

(i) _____

_____

(ii) _____

_____

(b) Write one sentence using both meanings of the word.

_____

_____

_____

List Words	Practise	Practise	D
automatic			
automobile			
autobiography			
autopsy			
circular			
circumstance			
circumference			
circumnavigate			
white			
sea			

Alphabetical Order

1. Write these words in alphabetical order.

    circumference   automobile

    circular   autobiography

    (a) _____

    (b) _____

    (c) _____

    (d) _____

Mirror Writing

2. Write the mirror written words correctly.

    (a) circular

    (b) autobiography

    (c) circumnavigate

    (d) white

Revision Words		
permission	monkey	microscope
manipulate	brunette	musical

All Mixed Up

3. Unjumble these list words.

    (a) saypout _____ (b) cauntsmircec _____

    (c) umalebooti _____ (d) lircacur _____

    (e) mutcoatia _____ (f) theiw _____

Difficult words I have found	Practise	Practise

4. Use list and revision words to solve the crossword.

Across

3. The measurement round a circle.

10. This type of car changes its own gear.

11. Ocean.

12. Car.

14. Examination of a corpse.

15. Brown-haired.

16. Ape.

Down

1. Situation.

2. An instrument to examine things with.

4. Round.

5. Go round the world by sea.

6. Consent.

7. Opposite to black.

8. The story of the author's life.

9. Manoeuvre.

13. Tuneful.

Word Hunt

5. (a) Which two words refer to colours? _____ _____

   (b) Which two words might a sailor use? _____ _____

   (c) A pathologist might perform this. _____

Shape Sorter

6. Write a list or revision word that fits in each shape.

(a)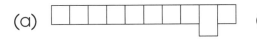

(b)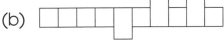

(c)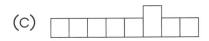

(d)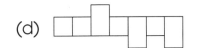

List Words	Practise	Practise	D
transmit			
transport			
translate			
transparent			
paradise			
parasite			
parachute			
paralysis			
began			
reference			

Alphabetical Order

1. Write these words in alphabetical order.

   transmit   transport

   transparent   translate

   (a) _____

   (b) _____

   (c) _____

   (d) _____

Incorrect Words

2. (a) parlisis   _____

   (b) referense   _____

   (c) parashute   _____

   (d) tranparent   _____

   (e) transpot   _____

Revision Words

extract	tunnel
microchip	market
manufacture	dumpling

Word Meanings

3. Match the words to their meanings.

   (a) paralysis   •   • to send by radio waves

   (b) paradise   •   • a letter about your abilities

   (c) reference   •   • powerless to move

   (d) transmit   •   • a wonderful place to go

Difficult words I have found	Practise	Practise

Unit 6

4. Use list and revision words to solve the wordsearch.

parachute   transmit

paradise   transport

paralysis   transparent

parasite   translate

began   reference

extract   tunnel

microchip   market

manufacture   dumpling

m	p	u	t	r	a	n	s	m	i	t	t	r
p	a	r	a	l	y	s	i	s	e	d	y	e
q	r	n	l	e	x	t	r	a	c	t	u	w
w	a	i	u	k	b	e	g	a	n	r	i	q
e	s	t	p	f	z	x	b	v	e	a	o	e
g	i	u	e	j	a	c	n	c	r	n	p	t
n	t	n	s	k	a	c	m	x	e	s	l	a
i	e	n	i	h	r	v	t	z	f	p	k	l
l	y	e	d	g	s	a	n	u	e	a	j	s
p	t	l	a	f	d	b	m	a	r	r	h	n
m	i	c	r	o	c	h	i	p	s	e	g	a
u	t	r	a	n	s	p	o	r	t	n	f	r
d	r	o	p	a	r	a	c	h	u	t	e	t

Mixed Up Sentences

5. Unjumble the sentences and write them below.

(a) paralysis in by parasite. the was The caused a herd

_____

(b) to tunnel. dangerous had the fumes They from the extract

_____

(c) radios. wrong the microchip used of The was in manufacture the

_____

(d) reference was the for sale book market. The on

_____

Verbs to Nouns

6. Change the nouns to verbs.

Verb	Noun	Noun
(a) transform	transformer	transformation
(b) transmit		
(c) translate		
(d) transport		

List Words	Practise	Practise	D
telephone			
telescope			
telepathy			
television			
interim			
interact			
interfere			
international			
took			
preparation			

Prefixes

1. Choose the correct prefix to make new words.

   inter   tele

   (a) _____ view

   (b) _____ port

   (c) _____ action

   (d) _____ graph

   (e) _____ com

Jumbled Words

3. Two words are jumbled together. Write the two words.

   (a) timtioonerk

   (b) tcinaeopteleserct

   _____   _____

   _____   _____

Revision Words

rifle

infantry

broken

microfilm

manual

baguette

Letters into Words

2. Write three list words using the letters on the television.

   _____

   _____

   _____

Difficult words I have found	Practise	Practise

4. Use list and revision words to solve the crossword.

Across

2. French bread roll.

4. Tiny camera spool.

5. Mind reading.

8. Worldwide.

11. A means of communication.

12. A type of gun.

14. Removed.

15. Foot soldiers.

Down

1. By hand.

3. Not working.

6. TV.

7. Making ready.

8. Meddle with.

9. You could look at the stars with this.

10. Short-term.

13. Intermingle.

Secret Words

5. (a) Change 'br' to 't' in broken.

_____

(b) Change 'vision' to 'gram' in television.

_____

(c) Change 'im' to 'com' in interim.

_____

(d) Change 'tele' to 'em' in telepathy.

_____

Secret Code

6. Use the secret code to find out the list or revision word.

a	e	f	i	k	l	m	n	o	r	s	t	v	y
1	2	3	4	5	6	7	8	9	10	11	12	13	14

(a) __ __ __ __ __ __ __
    4 8 12 2 10 4 7

(b) __ __ __ __ __ __ __ __ __
    4 8 3 1 8 12 10 14

(c) __ __ __ __
    12 9 9 5

(d) __ __ __ __ __ __ __ __ __
    12 2 6 2 13 4 11 4 9 8

(e) __ __ __ __ __
    10 4 3 6 2

List Words	Practise	Practise	D
happy			
puppy			
muddy			
gritty			
clothes			
farther			
birthday			
worthwhile			
done			
carry			

Changing Words

1. Change one letter in each word to make a list word.

   (a) buddy _____

   (b) dome _____

   (c) further _____

   (d) hippy _____

   (e) poppy _____

   (f) curry _____

Revision Words

critical	jewel
manuscript	turkey
practical	spectate

Small Words

2. Write a list word that contains these small words.

   (a) it _____

   (b) up _____

   (c) lot _____

   (d) art _____

   (e) on _____

   (f) or _____

   (g) her _____

   (h) day _____

   (i) the _____
   _____

   (j) car _____

Difficult words I have found	Practise	Practise

3. Use list and revision words to solve the wordsearch.

gritty   birthday

muddy   clothes

happy   farther

puppy   worthwhile

done   carry

critical   jewel

manuscript   turkey

practical   spectate

m	u	d	d	y	e	k	r	u	t	g	b	w
l	a	c	i	t	i	r	c	m	f	h	i	e
m	y	n	w	q	h	g	n	p	d	j	r	r
n	r	j	u	w	j	g	r	n	s	k	t	t
b	r	e	e	s	k	a	b	i	a	l	h	j
v	a	k	h	e	c	f	v	b	t	p	d	e
c	c	l	r	t	l	r	c	v	s	t	a	w
x	h	p	i	r	r	d	i	c	e	o	y	e
z	g	c	t	t	p	a	x	p	h	d	p	l
h	a	p	p	y	o	s	f	x	t	o	p	y
l	f	o	y	y	i	a	z	z	o	n	u	u
a	w	o	r	t	h	w	h	i	l	e	p	i
s	d	i	u	u	e	t	a	t	c	e	p	s

Missing Letters

4. Complete the list words.

(a) __ i __ __ __ __ a __   (b) __ o __ __ __ __ __ i __ e

(c) __ __ o __ __ e __   (d) __ a __ __ __

(e) __ a __ t __ __ __   (f) __ __ __ __

My Meanings

5. Write a definition for each of the list and revision words below. Use a dictionary to check your answers.

(a) gritty   _____

(b) worthwhile   _____

(c) farther   _____

(d) practical   _____

Comparisions

6. Complete the table.

(a)	cheeky	cheekier	cheekiest
(b)		happier	
(c)	muddy		
(d)			grittiest
(e)	far		

Revision Unit 2

List Words	Practise	Practise	D
necessary			
fulfil			
money			
reference			
diamond			
milk			
sea			
conscience			
began			
until			

All Mixed Up

1. Unjumble these revision words.

(a) menyo _____ (b) flufli _____

(c) freenecer _____ (d) mindado _____

(e) saysencer _____ (f) sinconceec _____

Missing Words

2. Complete using the revision words.

(a) She did not have enough _____ to buy the _____ ring.

(b) We cannot _____ the contract _____ the last brick is in place.

(c) It will be _____ to _____ the whole herd by hand!

(d) A _____ to the pollution in the _____ was in the newspaper.

Shape Sorter

3. Write a revision word that fits in each shape.

(a) [   ] (b) [   ] (c) [   ]

(d) [   ] (e) [   ] (f) [   ]

4. Find 12 mistakes and write them correctly on the lines.

As his mother's rferense to the selling of her dimond was on his consience,

_____

he bigan to deliver mulk he was prepared to do this untill he could save

_____

the nesessary muney to fullfil his desire to travel around the world by see.

_____

Word Hunt

5. (a) Which two words have four vowels?   _____

_____

(b) Which word names something made of carbon?   _____

(c) Which two words have only one syllable?   _____

_____

(d) Which word contains a number?   _____

Alphabetical Order

6. Write all the revision words in alphabetical order.

_____

_____

_____

Mixed Up Sentences

7. Unjumble the sentences and write them below.

(a) had money that buy I enough wish to I diamond.

_____

(b) had gave money The a conscience he the so guilty back. thief

_____

(c) lady to The wanted ambition sea. sail to the across an fulfil old

_____

List Words	Practise	Practise	D
really			
slowly			
quickly			
cheekily			
careful			
skilful			
colourful			
beautiful			
surprised			
once			

Base Words

1. Write the base words for each of these words.

(a) slowly   slow

(b) cheekily   _____

(c) colourful   _____

(d) beautiful   _____

Synonyms

2. Find a list word with a similar meaning.

(a) rudely   _____

(b) pretty   _____

(c) speedily   _____

(d) cautious   _____

(e) truly   _____

Revision Words	
area	graffiti
lady	child
automobile	transport

Word Worm Anagram

3. Choose every third letter and then rearrange them to make a list word.

bgithelpuawsntscgrsarplpchdnm

Difficult words I have found	Practise	Practise

Unit 9

ly ful

4. Use list and revision words to solve the crossword.

Across

2. Astonished.
5. On one occasion.
6. Cautious.
9. Bright.
10. Very pretty.
11. Gradually.
13. Adept.
14. Woman.

Down

1. Carry.
3. Region.
4. Car.
6. Young person.
7. Drawing on walls.
8. At speed.
9. Impertinently.
12. Truly.

Memory Master

5. (a) Cover the list and revision words. Write two from memory.

_____ _____

(b) For each word, write a question that has the word as its answer.

(i) _____

(ii) _____

Extend Yourself

6. (a) Use a dictionary to find two meanings for this word.

transport

(i) _____

(ii) _____

(b) Write one sentence using both meanings of the word.

_____

List Words	Practise	Practise	D
cinema			
circuit			
accident			
discipline			
cygnet			
cyclone			
cyclist			
mercy			
book			
scan			

Mirror Writing

1. Write the mirror written words correctly.

   (a) cyclist

   (b) accident

   (c) discipline

   (d) cyclone

Word Challenge

2. Make as many words as you can using letters from the word:

   discipline

   _____

   _____

   _____

Revision Words

interfere	gritty
circumstance	taxi
holiday	sheep

Word Hunt

3. (a) Which three words use the letter 'y' as a vowel?

   _____ _____

   _____

   (b) Which four words contain a 'soft c' and a 'hard c'?

   _____ _____

   _____ _____

Difficult words I have found	Practise	Practise

4. Use list and revision words to solve the wordsearch.

cinema	cygnet
circuit	cyclist
accident	mercy
discipline	cyclone
book	scan
interfere	gritty
circumstance	taxi
holiday	sheep

c	y	c	l	i	s	t	x	z	c	k	z	x
d	i	e	n	i	g	v	i	c	i	i	d	y
i	g	r	i	l	n	t	y	c	r	e	m	a
s	t	d	c	o	e	l	h	i	c	s	i	d
c	h	e	u	u	h	r	w	q	u	h	n	i
i	c	i	n	e	m	a	e	w	i	h	t	l
p	y	s	y	g	y	s	d	e	t	g	e	o
l	t	a	t	i	y	f	t	r	l	f	r	h
i	t	n	e	d	i	c	c	a	p	n	f	c
n	i	x	a	t	u	b	c	t	n	a	e	v
e	r	q	r	e	n	o	l	c	y	c	r	b
j	g	w	e	k	j	o	v	y	o	s	e	n
s	h	e	e	p	m	k	f	u	i	d	s	m

Missing Words

5. Use list or revision words to complete these sentences.

   (a) The chauffeur had an _____ on the _____ road.

   (b) Are you allowed to _____ all of that _____?

   (c) The _____ skidded on the last _____ of the race.

   (d) While on _____ we saw a great film at the local _____.

Magic Words

6. Change the first word into the last by changing one letter on each line to make a new word.

For example:

loaf	(a) scan	(b) book	(c) sheep
load	_____	_____	_____
lead	_____	_____	_____
head	boar	pout	bleed

List Words	Practise	Practise	D
corrupt			
curtain			
calendar			
document			
sure			
endure			
leisure			
pleasure			
circulate			
without			

Alphabetical Order

1. Write these words in alphabetical order.

   circulate   corrupt

   curtain   calendar

   (a) _____

   (b) _____

   (c) _____

   (d) _____

Revision Words

automatic	transmit
television	birthday
piano	emu

All Mixed Up

2. Unjumble these list words.

   (a) elerius   _____

   (b) ducmoent   _____

   (c) howtuti   _____

   (d) supareel   _____

   (e) dranclea   _____

Rhyming Words

3. Choose a rhyming word from the list.

   (a) argument   _____

   (b) disrupt   _____

   (c) about   _____

   (d) percolate   _____

Difficult words I have found	Practise	Practise

4. Use list and revision words to solve the crossword.

Across

2. Free time.

5. Lacking.

9. This gives you the date.

10. Drape.

12. This could be a type of engine.

13. Put up with.

14. Watch your favourite programme on this.

15. Musical instrument.

Down

1. Certain.

3. Large Australian bird.

4. Dishonest.

6. Broadcast.

7. Enjoyment.

8. Manuscript.

9. To move in a circle.

11. Date of birth.

Mixed Up Sentences

5. Unjumble the sentences and write them below.

(a) famine days had endure relief. for to many They without the

_____

(b) programme children. sure television suitable Make for young is that

_____

Proof Reading

6. Circle the incorrect words and write them correctly on the lines.

(a) Wash the curtin in the autamatic washing machine.

_____   _____

(b) Note in your calender the activity day at the liesure centre.

_____   _____

List Words	Practise	Practise	D
occur			
commit			
dip			
grin			
forget			
signal			
patrol			
expel			
second			
late			

Jumbled Words

1. Two words are jumbled together. Write the two words.

   (a) largsining

   _____

   _____

   (b) moltmicepex

   _____

   _____

Word Meanings

2. Match the words to their meanings.

   (a) occur •   • broad smile

   (b) grin   •   • do not remember

   (c) expel •   • not early

   (d) forget •   • throw out

   (e) late   •   • take place

Revision Words

gateway	tooth
circular	menu
telescope	puppy

Incorrect Words

3. (a) comit   _____

   (b) secund   _____

   (c) patroll   _____

   (d) ecepel   _____

   (e) lait   _____

Difficult words I have found	Practise	Practise

4. Use list and revision words to solve the wordsearch.

occur	commit
dip	grin
forget	signal
patrol	expel
second	late
gateway	tooth
circular	menu
telescope	puppy

l	t	n	m	g	g	w	s	m	j	u	i	n
p	k	e	r	a	l	u	c	r	i	c	i	l
o	j	b	l	t	y	q	t	n	i	r	s	p
i	l	a	t	e	t	a	i	b	g	n	l	l
u	h	v	l	w	s	z	m	h	t	o	o	t
y	r	c	p	a	e	c	m	g	k	d	r	m
p	u	p	p	y	c	f	o	r	g	e	t	k
t	c	x	o	v	o	s	c	p	j	y	a	i
r	c	z	k	b	n	e	d	t	e	t	p	j
e	o	a	m	h	d	r	x	i	x	s	a	u
w	g	e	m	h	f	d	c	r	p	t	q	y
q	n	s	n	i	c	x	v	f	e	c	w	t
u	f	d	j	s	i	g	n	a	l	v	e	r

Secret Words

5. (a) Change 'pa' to 'con' in patrol.

_____

(b) Change 'tele' to 'micro' in telescope.

_____

(c) Change 'oc' to 're' in occur.

_____

(d) Change 'com' to 'sub' in commit.

_____

(e) Change 'ond' to 'ure' in second.

_____

Change the Tense

6. Complete these list words.

(a)	expel	expelling	expelled
(b)	commit		
(c)	occur		
(d)	grin		
(e)	dip		
(f)	signal		
(g)	patrol		

List Words	Practise	Practise	D
vein			
weird			
either			
beige			
sleigh			
heir			
rein			
reign			
Miss			
idea			

Missing Letters

1. Complete the list word.

   (a) __ __ e __ __ __

   (b) e __ __ __ e __

   (c) __ e __ __ e

   (d) __ i __ __

   (e) r __ __ __

Revision Words

agenda	Peru	display
mouse	parachute	telephone

Letters into Words

2. Write three list words using the letters on the bubble.

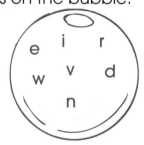

_____

_____

_____

Shape Sorter

3. Write a list word that fits in each shape.

   (a)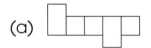

   (b)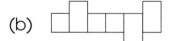

   (c)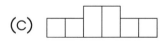

   (d)

Difficult words I have found	Practise	Practise

4. Use list and revision words to solve the crossword.

Across

1. Small rodent.
4. Put on show.
7. A list of things to do.
8. One or another.
9. Essential for a safe landing.
12. Rule.
13. He will inherit.
14. Very strange.

Down

1. Unmarried woman.
2. Brainwave.
3. Sled.
5. Taupe.
6. Many people have a mobile one.

9. A South American country.
10. Leash.
11. Blood flows through this.

Secret Code

5. Use the secret code to find out the list or revision word.

a	c	d	e	g	h	i	l	n	o	p	r	t	u	v
1	2	3	4	5	6	7	8	9	10	11	12	13	14	15

(a) __ __ __ __ __ __
  1 5 4 9 3 1

(b) __ __ __ __ __
  12 4 7 5 9

(c) __ __ __ __
  15 4 7 9

(d) __ __ __ __ __ __ __ __
  11 1 12 1 2 6 14 13 4

(e) __ __ __ __ __ __ __ __ __
  13 4 8 4 11 6 10 9 4

Homophones

6. Circle and write the correct word.

(a) Slay/Sleigh the caribou and bring it home on the slay/sleigh.

_____ _____

(b) The vain/vein lord thought blue blood flowed through his vains/veins.

_____ _____

List Words	Practise	Practise	D
shield			
pierce			
diesel			
patient			
deceit			
conceit			
receipt			
perceive			
atmosphere			
eat			

Mirror Writing

1. Write the mirror written words correctly.

   (a) patient

   (b) diesel

   (c) pierce

   (d) conceit

Word Challenge

2. Make as many words as you can using letters from the word:

   atmosphere

   _____   _____

   _____   _____

   _____   _____

   _____   Number of words [ ]

Revision Words

worthwhile	hero
macaroni	baby
die	transparent

Word Worm Anagram

3. Choose every third letter and then rearrange them to make a list word.

njertepotserwtiaspoicvb

Difficult words I have found	Practise	Practise

4. Use list and revision words to solve the wordsearch.

shield	perceive
pierce	receipt
diesel	deceit
patient	conceit
atmosphere	eat
worthwhile	hero
macaroni	baby
die	transparent

w	o	r	t	h	w	h	i	l	e	g	i	h
t	r	e	n	e	w	q	a	s	d	f	n	c
y	d	s	p	i	e	r	c	e	x	d	o	t
d	c	h	e	x	n	t	c	a	d	n	r	b
i	v	i	e	r	b	r	r	q	c	a	a	j
e	h	e	r	o	e	l	e	e	n	b	c	r
s	c	l	c	o	c	h	i	s	y	w	a	e
e	m	d	e	h	f	t	p	s	x	c	m	c
l	j	d	h	g	f	a	d	s	s	a	d	e
k	l	p	o	e	r	e	i	u	o	y	t	i
p	e	r	c	e	i	v	e	j	h	m	g	p
c	x	z	n	a	s	d	e	c	e	i	t	t
p	a	t	i	e	n	t	c	v	b	n	m	a

My Meanings

5. Write a definition for each of these words. Use a dictionary to check your answers.

(a) conceit _____

(b) shield _____

(c) deceit _____

(d) transparent _____

(e) perceive _____

(f) macaroni _____

(g) pierce _____

Extend Yourself

6. (a) This word can be used as a noun or an adjective. Write a definition for each.

patient

(i) _____

(ii) _____

(b) Write one sentence using both meanings of the word.

_____

_____

List Words	Practise	Practise	D
range			
grange			
arrange			
derange			
dance			
trance			
romance			
enhance			
business			
proportion			

Revision Words

interact	farther
umbrella	spaghetti
enemy	scissors

Small Words

1. Write a list word that contains these small words.

(a) gran   _____

(b) sin   _____

(c) port   _____

(d) man   _____

All Mixed Up

2. Unjumble these list words.

(a) acromen   _____

(b) toopinpror   _____

(c) cheanne   _____

(d) reggna   _____

(e) nisebuss   _____

(f) rageanr   _____

Word Hunt

3. (a) Which two list words have a double consonant?

   _____

   _____

(b) Which word has a silent 'i'?

   _____

Difficult words I have found	Practise	Practise

4. Use list and revision words to solve the crossword.

Across

1. Percentage.
5. Ballet is one type of this.
8. Add to.
10. Farm.
11. A type of pasta.
13. Love affair.
14. Trade.
15. Foe.

Down

2. Scope.
3. Daydream.
4. It keeps the rain off.
6. More distant.
7. Unhinge mentally.
9. Cooperate.
11. Use these to cut paper.
12. Set out.

Memory Master

5. (a) Cover the list and revision words. Write two from memory.

_____　_____

(b) For each word, write a question that has the word as its answer.

(i) _____

(ii) _____

Missing Words

6. Use list or revision words to complete these sentences.

(a) After the _____ we went to a restaurant for

_____.

(b) His _____ cut his brake cable with a sharp pair of

_____!

(c) She declared that her _____ was none of his

_____.

List Words	Practise	Practise	D
course			
coarse			
stair			
stare			
flare			
flair			
cereal			
serial			
energy			
India			

Alphabetical Order

1. Write these words in alphabetical order.

    stare   coarse

    course   stair

(a) _____

(b) _____

(c) _____

(d) _____

Changing Words

3. Change one letter in each word to make a list word.

(a) aerial   _____

(c) share   _____

Revision Words		
autopsy	paralysis	international
tomato	key	foot

Synonyms

2. Find a list word with a similar meaning.

(a) route   _____

(b) step   _____

(c) talent   _____

(d) gaze   _____

(b) flame   _____

(d) hoarse   _____

Difficult words I have found	Practise	Practise

4. Use list and revision words to solve the wordsearch.

course	coarse
stair	stare
flare	flair
cereal	serial
energy	India
autopsy	paralysis
international	tomato
key	foot

l	n	d	i	a	w	d	e	r	t	c	y	u
e	n	e	r	g	y	n	m	k	o	o	l	i
r	q	t	s	e	d	c	v	f	r	u	p	o
a	a	j	e	j	m	n	h	y	p	r	l	p
t	z	i	r	r	p	c	o	a	r	s	e	l
s	x	u	i	u	n	s	r	r	t	e	p	k
m	s	h	a	i	o	a	o	s	y	y	o	j
n	w	f	l	k	l	d	t	t	s	e	k	c
b	e	l	q	y	l	a	a	i	p	h	k	e
v	d	a	s	w	i	e	m	r	o	n	m	r
c	c	i	b	r	v	f	o	o	t	n	n	e
x	s	r	v	f	r	t	t	g	u	b	a	a
z	a	s	d	f	g	h	e	r	a	l	f	l

Mixed Up Sentences

5. Unjumble the sentences and write them below.

(a) have to course. He enough challenging the not energy did complete

_____

(b) setting was romantic the the serial. perfect India television for

_____

(c) had man cereal. put to I stare who tomato his at the on

_____

(d) paralysis her fell stairs. down She in she foot had after the

_____

Homophones

6. Circle and write the words in the correct order.

(a) The serial/cereal killer always ate serial/cereal at midnight.

_____ _____

(b) She liked to sit on the stare/stair and stare/stair at the guests.

_____ _____

(c) In the coarse/course of his work, he had to cut coarse/course material.

_____ _____

Revision Unit 3

List Words	Practise	Practise	D
circulate			
second			
surprised			
proportion			
once			
without			
late			
atmosphere			
business			
India			

All Mixed Up

1. Unjumble these revision words. Some of these letters will be capitals.

   (a) disperrus   _____ (b) homepestar _____

   (c) socden   _____ (d) caticruel   _____

   (e) adiin   _____ (f) cone   _____

Missing Words

2. Complete using the revision words.

   (a) In the course of _____ he had to travel to _____.

   (b) A small _____ of the _____ is comprised of nitrogen.

   (c) They reached the hospital _____ a _____ to spare.

   (d) I was _____ to hear that my gran had _____ been a pilot.

Shape Sorter

3. Write a revision word that fits in each shape.

   (a)   (b)

   (c)   (d)

4. Find 12 mistakes and write them correctly on the lines.

He was suprised at the atmosfere when tried to circolate among a

preporation of friends he had onse met with his lait wife. Washout their

friendship, he and his sekond wife opted start a new busnes in india.

Word Hunt

5. (a) Which three words have only two vowels? _____

_____

_____

(b) Which word is a compound word? _____

(c) Which word can be an adjective or a noun? _____

Alphabetical Order

6. Write all the revision words in alphabetical order.

_____

_____

_____

Mixed Up Sentences

7. Unjumble the sentences and write them below.

(a) athletics. well the in second to India come did

_____

(b) too business woman meeting. arrived for The late her

_____

(c) atmosphere room The me. the unpleasant in surprised

_____

List Words	Practise	Practise	D
media			
medicine			
mediocre			
medium			
midnight			
midway			
midriff			
midwife			
real			
almost			

Jumbled Words

1. Two words are jumbled together. Write the two words.

   (a) cineemadmidie

   _____

   _____

   (b) hitmaydimdignw

   _____

   _____

Incorrect Words

3. (a) midwive _____ (b) midia _____

   (c) medum _____ (d) medeocer _____

   (e) medisin _____ (f) midnite _____

Revision Words

quickly	circuit	document
patrol	weird	receipt

Word Meanings

2. Match the words to their meanings.

   (a) mediocre • • very nearly

   (b) midriff • • actually existing

   (c) almost • • part between your waist and chest

   (d) real • • moderate to inferior in quality

Difficult words I have found	Practise	Practise

4. Use list and revision words to solve the crossword.

Across

1. Nearly.
5. Manuscript.
7. Lap.
9. Halfway.
10. Genuine.
11. Second-rate.
12. This person delivers babies.
13. Proof of payment.
14. Television and press.

Down

2. Middling.
3. Very strange.
4. At speed.
6. Your middle.
8. Tour of duty.
9. Twelve hours after noon.
11. A doctor prescribes this.

Secret Words

5. (a) Change 'um' to 'ate' in medium.

_____

(b) Change 'ckly' to 'bble' in quickly.

_____

(c) Change 'ocre' to 'tate' in mediocre.

_____

(d) Change 'pa' to 'con' in patrol.

_____

Secret Code

6. Use the secret code to find out the list or revision word.

a	c	d	e	i	l	m	n	p	r	t	u
1	2	3	4	5	6	7	8	9	10	11	12

(a) __ __ __ __ __ __
7 4 3 5 12 7

(b) __ __ __ __
10 4 1 6

(c) __ __ __ __ __ __ __
2 5 10 2 12 5 11

(d) __ __ __ __ __ __ __ __
7 4 3 5 2 5 8 4

(e) __ __ __ __ __ __ __
10 4 2 4 5 9 11

List Words	Practise	Practise	D
destroy			
noisy			
tidy			
lazy			
copy			
ready			
buy			
easy			
Greece			
above			

Adverbs

1. Change the adjectives to adverbs.

Adjectives	Adverb
(a) easy	easily
(b) lazy	_____
(c) noisy	_____
(d) ready	_____
(e) tidy	_____

Rhyming Words

3. Add an ending to a list word to make it rhyme.

   (a) sneezing   easing

   (b) enjoying   _____

   (c) crying   _____

   (d) gazing   _____

Word Worm

2. Circle four list words with an ending added, written backwards in the word worm.

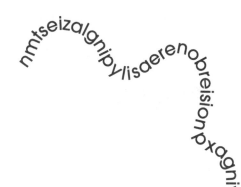

Difficult words I have found	Practise	Practise

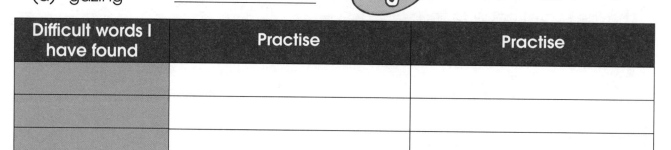

4. Use list and revision words to solve the wordsearch.

destroy   noisy

tidy   lazy

copy   ready

buy   easy

Greece   above

grange   cereal

slowly   accident

leisure   commit

m	n	a	b	v	c	x	z	a	s	d	f	g
t	y	u	c	i	o	p	e	g	n	a	r	G
r	n	o	e	c	b	v	c	x	z	a	l	r
e	p	q	r	w	i	e	r	t	y	s	k	e
y	l	w	e	k	j	d	h	l	y	s	a	e
l	a	e	a	s	a	q	e	g	d	u	a	c
w	z	r	l	y	s	i	o	n	i	d	b	e
o	y	o	r	t	s	e	d	f	t	f	o	h
l	m	t	l	u	p	o	i	u	i	g	v	j
s	n	y	r	e	a	d	y	d	m	h	e	k
w	b	e	i	u	o	p	l	k	m	j	j	l
q	v	c	x	z	a	s	d	f	o	g	h	p
w	d	e	f	r	g	t	h	y	c	u	i	o

5. Find a list or revision word with an opposite meaning.

(a) quickly   _____

(b) work   _____

(c) sell   _____

(d) difficult   _____

(e) create   _____

(f) below   _____

(g) quiet   _____

(h) messy   _____

Comparisons

6. Complete these list words.

(a) happy	happier	happiest
(b) tidy		
(c) lazy		
(d) noisy		
(e) easy		

Revision Words

grange

cereal

slowly

accident

leisure

commit

List Words	Practise	Practise	D
chief			
alien			
achieve			
society			
belief			
science			
hygiene			
relieve			
Australia			
sometimes			

Small Words

1. Write a list word that contains these small words.

   (a) us _____

   (b) met _____

   (c) lie _____

   _____

More Nouns

2. Change these list words to nouns that name people.

   (a) botany   botanist

   (b) science _____

   (c) hygiene _____

   (d) Australia _____

Word Worm Anagram

3. Choose every third letter and then rearrange them to make a list word.

Revision Words		
either	trance	stair
skilful	cygnet	endure

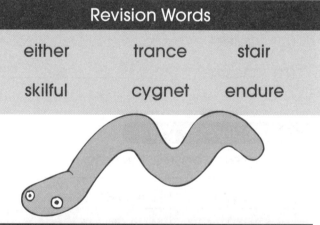

Difficult words I have found	Practise	Practise

4. Use list and revision words to solve the crossword.

Across

1. Physics is one branch of this.
3. Hypnotic state.
6. Step.
7. Country between the Pacific and Indian Oceans.
8. On occasion.
9. Main.
10. Foreign.
13. Cleanliness.
14. Be successful.

Down

1. Dexterous.
2. Put up with.
4. Ease.
5. Whichever.
8. Culture.
11. Baby swan.
12. Faith.

Word Hunt

5. (a) Which word is a compound word?

_____

(b) Which verb adds 'ment' to make a noun?

_____

(c) Which two words use a 'y' for a vowel?

_____

(d) Which word is a homophone?

_____

(e) Which word could change its last two letters to an 'f' to make a new word?

_____

Extend Yourself

6. This word can be used as a noun or an adjective. Write a sentence for each.

alien

(a) _____

(b) _____

in *im*

Unit 20

List Words	Practise	Practise	D
inactive			
inaccurate			
inconvenient			
incapable			
impatient			
immobile			
impolite			
immature			
mountain			
chocolate			

Alphabetical Order

1. Put the list words with the 'im' sound in alphabetical order.

_____

_____

_____

_____

Mirror Writing

2. Write the mirror written words correctly.

(a) impatient

(b) chocolate

(c) incapable

(d) inactive

(e) immobile

Making Adverbs

3. Add 'ly' to these words to make adverbs. Write the new word. Use a dictionary to check the spelling.

	Word	adverb 'ly'
(a)	inaccurate	
(b)	impatient	
(c)	inconvenient	
(d)	impolite	

Difficult words I have found	Practise	Practise

Unit 20 *in*   *im*

4. Use list and revision words to solve the wordsearch.

inactive	immature
inaccurate	immobile
inconvenient	impolite
incapable	impatient
mountain	chocolate
occur	shield
derange	careful
cyclone	tractor

i	n	a	c	c	u	r	a	t	e	z	i
n	x	c	a	r	e	f	u	l	v	i	n
c	h	o	c	o	l	a	t	e	b	n	c
o	c	c	u	r	t	y	j	x	w	a	a
n	m	o	u	n	t	a	i	n	s	c	p
v	q	c	y	c	l	o	n	e	h	t	a
e	i	m	p	o	l	i	t	e	i	i	b
n	d	i	m	m	o	b	i	l	e	v	l
i	m	m	a	t	u	r	e	k	l	e	e
e	d	e	r	a	n	g	e	g	d	h	p
n	c	j	i	m	p	a	t	i	e	n	t
t	r	a	c	t	o	r	w	x	z	q	k

My Meanings

5. Write a definition for each of these words. Use a dictionary to check your answers.

(a) cyclone _____

(b) mountain _____

(c) incapable _____

(d) immature _____

(e) impatient _____

(f) inconvenient _____

Missing Words

6. Use list or revision words to complete these sentences.

(a) It was so cold on the

_____, he was _____

to return to his chalet for a cup of hot _____.

(b) The _____ is _____, however

he is _____ of fixing it.

(c) The weather report was _____ and did not

warn people about the _____.

Revision Words

occur

shield

derange

careful

cyclone

tractor

List Words	Practise	Practise	D
irregular			
irrational			
irresponsible			
irresistible			
illegal			
illiterate			
illegible			
illusion			
thirty			
forty			

Word Hunt

1. Write down four list words which end with a vowel.

_____
_____
_____
_____

Word Worm

2. (a) Circle the words you find in the word worm.

illusionfortyenhancecinemailliteratesignalirresponsibledeceit

(b) Write the eight words that are not in the word worm.

_____
_____
_____
_____
_____
_____
_____
_____

Small Words

3. Find small words.

(a) illegal

_____
_____

(b) illiterate

_____
_____

(c) forty

_____

Difficult words I have found	Practise	Practise

4. Use list and revision words to solve the crossword.

Across

7. Vivid.
8. Reckless.
9. Ten less than fifty.
10. Three times ten.
12. Rule.
13. Unlawful.
14. To make more attractive.
15. Unreadable.

Down

1. Extremely desirable.
2. Created by a magician.
3. Unable to read or write.
4. Uneven.
5. Dishonesty.
6. Behaving in an unreasonable way.
7. We went to the

   _____

   to see a film.
11. Sign.

Revision Words

signal

reign

deceit

enhance

colourful

cinema

Extend Yourself

5. Find two more words with the prefix 'ir' and two more with the prefix 'il'.

_____

_____

_____

Word Challenge

6. Make as many words as you can using letters from the word:

irresistible

_____   _____

_____   _____

_____   _____

_____   _____

_____   _____

Number of words [ ]

List Words	Practise	Practise	D
magician			
optician			
politician			
barbarian			
deletion			
depletion			
completion			
discretion			
young			
icon			

Base Words

1. Find the base words for the following words.

   (a) deletion　　delete

   (b) completion _____

   (c) discretion　_____

   (d) depletion　_____

All Mixed Up

2. Unjumble these list words.

   (a) ctaipnoi　_____

   (b) uygon　　_____

   (c) ncio　　　_____

   (d) rabbianar　_____

   (e) acinmiag　_____

   (f) leondtie　_____

Match Endings

3. Match the beginnings to the endings. Write the word.

   (a) com • • ician _____

   (b) mag • • arian _____

   (c) barb • • etion _____

   (d) discr • • pletion _____

   (e) cur • • ient _____

   (f) pat • • tain _____

Difficult words I have found	Practise	Practise

4. Use list and revision words to solve the wordsearch.

depletion   optician

magician   barbarian

politician   discretion

completion   deletion

young   icon

curtain   forget

vein   patient

range   beautiful

d	d	i	s	c	r	e	t	i	o	n	p
b	a	r	b	a	r	i	a	n	q	w	o
e	n	s	f	z	y	i	z	a	m	n	l
a	i	n	d	e	l	e	t	i	o	n	i
u	e	o	t	i	k	l	v	c	v	g	t
t	v	c	o	p	t	i	c	i	a	n	i
i	x	i	f	j	m	o	j	g	r	u	c
f	o	r	g	e	t	b	u	a	a	o	i
u	c	u	r	t	a	i	n	m	n	y	a
l	s	p	a	t	i	e	n	t	g	d	n
d	e	p	l	e	t	i	o	n	e	q	j
v	c	o	m	p	l	e	t	i	o	n	d

Missing Words

5. Use list or revision words to complete these sentences.

(a) The _____ pulled a rabbit out of the hat.

(b) A lamb is a _____ sheep.

(c) He went to the _____ for new glasses.

(d) The workmen were paid on _____ of the job.

(e) He clicked on the Internet _____.

(f) The _____ had a sore _____.

(g) The shop has a _____ _____ of curtains.

Revision Words

curtain

forget

vein

patient

range

beautiful

Memory Master

6. (a) Cover the list words. Write three from memory.

_____

_____

_____

(b) Use each of these words in a sentence.

_____

_____

_____.

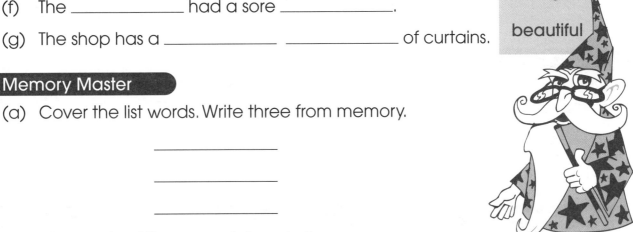

List Words	Practise	Practise	D
motion			
potion			
devotion			
promotion			
solution			
pollution			
revolution			
distribution			
fifty			
sixty			

Jumbled Words

1. Two words are jumbled together. Write the two words.

   (a) notetinvopiodo

   _____

   _____

   (b) roomvoontietulin

   _____

   _____

Nouns to Verbs

2. Change the nouns to verbs.

Nouns	Verbs
(a) solution	
(b) promotion	
(c) distribution	
(d) pollution	

Revision Words

disciple	pleasure	dip
perceive	romance	serial

Changing Words

3. Change one letter in each word to make a list word.

   (a) resolution _____   (b) sixth _____

   (c) demotion _____   (d) nifty _____

Difficult words I have found	Practise	Practise

4. Use list and revision words to solve the crossword.

Across

2. Giving out.
7. Half of one hundred.
8. Raise in position at work.
9. Dedication.
10. Answer to a problem.
12. Delight.
14. Movement.
15. Entertainment in instalments.

Down

1. Love story.
3. Rotation.
4. Devoted follower.
5. Brew.
6. Plunge.
8. Contamination.
11. See.
13. 5 times 12.

Word Challenge

5. Make as many words as you can using letters from the word:

revolution

_____

_____

_____

_____

_____

_____

Word Hunt

6. (a) Which two words have four syllables?

_____ _____

(b) Which two words name multiples of ten?

_____ _____

(c) Find four rhyming words.

_____ _____

_____ _____

(d) Find four more rhyming words.

_____ _____

_____ _____

List Words	Practise	Practise	D
nation			
education			
translation			
stationery			
position			
repetition			
intuition			
competition			
seen			
Africa			

Small Words

1. Write a list word that contains these small words.

   (a) cat   _____

   (b) ran   _____

   (c) one   _____

   (d) sit   _____

Word Worm Anagram

3. Choose every third letter and then rearrange them to make a list word.

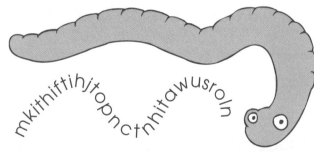

Revision Words		
really	cyclist	corrupt
expel	pierce	arrange

Nouns to Verbs

2. Change the nouns to verbs.

Nouns	Verbs
(a) translation	
(b) competition	
(c) repetition	
(d) education	
(e) cyclist	

Difficult words I have found	Practise	Practise

4. Use list and revision words to solve the wordsearch.

repetition   nation

competition   stationery

position   education

intuition   translation

seen   Africa

really   cyclist

corrupt   expel

pierce   arrange

e	x	p	e	l	l	k	j	h	g	f	d	t
g	p	p	s	t	a	t	i	o	n	e	r	y
n	o	o	k	r	j	h	g	f	d	a	e	s
a	o	s	q	n	e	e	s	w	n	c	p	a
r	i	i	w	k	o	a	l	s	e	y	e	z
r	u	t	t	j	n	i	l	p	r	c	t	x
A	y	i	e	i	d	a	t	l	t	l	i	c
f	t	o	r	h	t	s	t	i	y	i	t	e
r	r	n	t	i	g	e	f	i	u	s	i	c
i	e	l	o	y	u	i	p	o	o	t	o	r
c	w	n	p	o	i	u	y	m	y	n	n	e
a	q	e	d	u	c	a	t	i	o	n	s	i
m	n	b	v	t	p	u	r	r	o	c	a	p

My Meanings

5. Write a definition for each of the list and revision words below. Use a dictionary to check your answers.

(a) stationery _____

(b) corrupt _____

(c) nation _____

(d) intuition _____

(e) expel _____

(f) pierce _____

Missing Words

6. Use list or revision words to complete these sentences.

(a) Could you _____ to have that _____ file removed from my computer?

(b) The _____ was exhausted after winning the _____.

(c) Kenya is a _____ in _____.

(d) The secretary asked me to _____ for more _____ to be delivered.

Revision Unit 4

List Words	Practise	Practise	D
thirty			
almost			
sometimes			
chocolate			
mountain			
forty			
icon			
sixty			
Africa			
above			

All Mixed Up

1. Unjumble these revision words. Some of these letters will be capitals.

   (a) nico _____

   (b) rafcai _____

   (c) tomsal _____

   (d) nunomait _____

   (e) tryhit _____

   (f) coalthoce _____

Missing Words

2. Complete using the revision words.

   (a) _____ I eat too much _____.

   (b) _____ all else, I would like to visit _____.

   (c) That _____ is _____ two hundred years old.

   (d) Is he too old at _____ to climb that _____?

Shape Sorter

3. Write a revision word that fits in each shape.

4. Find 12 mistakes and write them correctly on the lines.

Sumtimes I do'nt concentrate! I allmost sent a mountin chocalate to

_____

africa. Thurty, fortey or even sixtay companies abuv the equator

_____

would have received the products with just a click on an akon.

_____

Word Hunt

5. (a) In the list, find three adverbs.

_____   _____

_____

(b) Find three words with only one vowel.

_____   _____

_____

(c) Which words end in vowels?

_____   _____

_____

Alphabetical Order

6. Write all the revision words in alphabetical order.

_____

_____

_____

_____

_____

_____

_____

_____

_____

_____

Mixed Up Sentences

7. Unjumble the sentences and write them below.

(a) clouds. we the the above climbed went When mountain we

_____

(b) was to When he Africa. man live went the in forty

_____

(c) if makes and that thirty Did you sixty? know add it thirty you

_____

List Words	Practise	Practise	D
miserable			
voluntary			
definitely			
familiar			
desperate			
original			
jewellery			
library			
China			
leave			

Antonyms

1. Find a list word with an opposite meaning.

   (a) arrive _____

   (b) compulsory _____

   (c) happy _____

   (d) possibly _____

Adverbs

2. Change the adjectives to adverbs.

Adjectives	Adverb
(a) miserable	_____
(b) original	_____
(c) desperate	_____
(d) voluntary	_____

Mirror Writing

3. Write the mirror written words correctly.

   (a) library

   (b) jewellery

   (c) voluntary

   (d) desperate

   (e) familiar

Revision Words

media	destroy
society	impolite
illegal	optician

Difficult words I have found	Practise	Practise

4. Use list and revision words to solve the crossword.

Across

4. At the end of your tether.
9. Innovative.
10. Rude.
11. A country in Asia.
12. Unlawful.
14. A large room for books.
15. Wretched.

Down

1. Ruin.
2. An 'eye doctor'.
3. The press.
4. Surely.
5. Culture.

6. Well-known.
7. Of your free will.
8. Personal ornaments.
13. Go.

Missing Letters

5. Fill in the missing vowels.

(a) v __ l __ n t __ r y

(b) l __ b r __ r y

(c) d __ f __ n __ t __ l y

(d) m __ s __ r __ b l __

(e) d __ s p __ r __ t __

(f) __ r __ g __ n __ l

(g) j __ w __ l l __ r y

(h) f __ m __ l __ __ r

Extend Yourself

6. (a) This word can be used as a noun or an abjective. Write a definition for each.

China

(i) _____

(ii) _____

(b) Write one sentence using both meanings of the word.

_____

List Words	Practise	Practise	D
giraffe			
gigantic			
region			
religion			
gypsy			
gymnasium			
Egypt			
allergy			
seventy			
eighty			

Incorrect Words

1. (a) regin _____

    (b) alergy _____

    (c) jimnasium _____

    (d) girafe _____

    (e) gygantic _____

Alphabetical Order

2. Put the words beginning with 'g' in alphabetical order.

_____

_____

_____

_____

Revision Words

revolution	intuition	mediocre
copy	hygiene	incapable

All Mixed Up

3. Unjumble the list words.

    (a) geriloni _____   (b) farefig _____

    (c) sypyg _____   (d) tincaggi _____

    (e) larygel _____   (f) venyest _____

Difficult words I have found	Practise	Practise

4. Use list and revision words to solve the wordsearch.

giraffe	gymnasium
gigantic	gypsy
religion	Egypt
region	allergy
seventy	eighty
revolution	intuition
mediocre	copy
hygiene	incapable

r	e	g	i	o	n	o	i	g	i	l	e	r
m	i	k	l	i	h	y	g	i	e	n	e	o
n	g	j	h	n	p	o	i	u	y	v	l	p
e	i	g	v	t	b	n	y	p	o	c	b	l
b	r	f	c	u	j	h	m	l	g	g	a	k
v	a	c	x	i	k	o	u	t	y	m	p	j
a	f	d	o	t	l	t	i	p	f	m	a	h
l	f	s	z	i	i	p	s	y	d	n	c	g
l	e	a	a	o	d	y	a	g	s	b	n	f
e	u	z	n	n	x	e	n	E	c	v	i	d
r	y	t	r	e	w	q	m	q	w	e	r	s
g	s	e	v	e	n	t	y	t	h	g	i	e
y	c	x	z	a	g	i	g	a	n	t	i	c

Memory Master

5. (a) Cover the list and revision words. Write two from memory.

_____ _____

(b) For each word, write a question that has the word as its answer.

(i) _____

_____

(ii) _____

_____

Mixed Up Sentences

6. Unjumble the sentences and write them below.

(a) has has hygiene he He allergy. be as about particular an to

_____

_____

(b) remote in to region Egypt. She travelled a

_____

(c) least eighty the giraffes or We seventy on saw at safari.

_____

(d) gigantic in swimming built gymnasium. the have a They pool

_____

List Words	Practise	Practise	D
proactive			
project			
produce			
propeller			
suspect			
suspicion			
suspend			
sustain			
ninety			
hundred			

Rhyming Words

1. Find a list word that rhymes.

   (a) cellar _____

   (b) depend _____

   (c) reduce _____

   (d) remission _____

Revision Words

illegible	completion
potion	competition
lazy	alien

Letters into Words

2. Write three list words using the letters on the boat.

   _____

   _____

   _____

Small Words

3. Write a list word that contains these small words.

   (a) net _____

   (b) rope _____

   (c) rod _____

   (d) pen _____

   (e) act _____

Difficult words I have found	Practise	Practise

4. Use list and revision words to solve the crossword.

Across

1. Create.
5. Keep up.
7. It is found beneath the boat.
9. Task.
12. Rivalry.
14. Unreadable.

Down

2. He may be guilty.
3. Ten less than one hundred.
4. Doubt.
6. Finishing.
7. Takes initiative.
8. Hang.
10. Century.
11. Brew.
13. From another planet.
15. Idle.

Secret Words

5. (a) Change 'sus' to 'ob' in sustain.

_____

(b) Change 'y' to 'een' in ninety.

_____

(c) Change 'on' to 've' in competition.

_____

(d) Change 'dr' to 't' in hundred.

_____

Secret Code

6. Use the secret code to find out the list or revision word.

a	c	d	e	i	l	n	o	p	r	s	t	u	v
1	2	3	4	5	6	7	8	9	10	11	12	13	14

(a) __ __ __ __ __ __
   9   8 12   5   8   7

(b) __ __ __ __ __
   1   6   5   4   7

(c) __ __ __ __ __ __ __
  11 13 11   9   4   7   3

(d) __ __ __ __ __ __ __ __ __
  11 13 11   9   5   2   5   8   7

(e) __ __ __ __ __ __ __ __ __
   9 10   8   1   2 12   5 14   4

List Words	Practise	Practise	D
physics			
physical			
physique			
pharmacy			
emphasis			
phobia			
apostrophe			
catastrophe			
family			
body			

Jumbled Words

1. Two words are jumbled together. Write the two words.

   (a) abbodhopiy

   _____

   _____

   (b) flamepashisimy

   _____

   _____

Revision Words	
inactive	illusion
magician	devotion
repetition	buy

Word Meanings

2. Match the words to their meanings.

   (a) physique • • great fear of something

   (b) pharmacy • • stress on a word or part of a word

   (c) emphasis • • dispensary

   (d) phobia • • a person's build

Word Challenge

3. Make as many words as you can using letters from the word:

   catastrophe

   _____

   _____

   _____

Difficult words I have found	Practise	Practise

4. Use list and revision words to solve the wordsearch.

physics   physical

physique   pharmacy

emphasis   phobia

apostrophe   catastrophe

family   body

inactive   illusion

magician   devotion

repetition   buy

e	m	p	h	a	s	i	s	j	h	g	f	c
m	k	l	y	c	a	m	r	a	h	p	a	d
n	l	e	b	v	b	c	e	x	z	t	p	s
b	p	p	h	o	z	p	p	x	a	a	o	a
v	o	h	d	p	h	d	e	s	c	e	i	i
l	i	y	n	o	o	a	t	s	v	s	u	l
a	u	s	b	u	y	r	i	i	v	d	y	l
c	y	i	m	n	o	i	t	o	v	e	d	u
i	a	q	m	p	n	c	i	s	b	f	t	s
s	t	u	h	k	a	j	o	h	o	g	r	i
y	r	e	e	n	w	q	n	q	w	p	e	o
h	c	x	i	z	m	a	g	i	c	i	a	n
p	h	y	s	i	c	s	y	l	i	m	a	f

My Meanings

5. Write a definition for each of these words. Use a dictionary to check your answers.

(a) catastrophe _____

(b) physical _____

(c) illusion _____

(d) devotion _____

(e) apostrophe _____

Proof-reading

6. Circle and incorrect words and write them correctly on the lines.

(a) The majician created the ilusion of sawing the body in half.

_____ _____

(b) After the catastraphe the demand on the farmacy was immense.

_____ _____

(c) Due to his innactive lifestyle the man had a plump phisique.

_____ _____

(d) I am hoping my familie will by me a bike for Christmas.

_____ _____

List Words	Practise	Practise	D
perspire			
pertinent			
persuade			
permit			
window			
arrow			
widow			
follow			
music			
colour			

Revision Words

belief	inconvenient
irregular	medicine
solution	translation

Verbs to Nouns

2. Complete the table. You may use a dictionary.

Verb	Noun
(a) perforate	perforation
(b) perspire	
(c) persuade	
(d) permit	

Antonyms

1. Find a list word with an opposite meaning.

   (a) dissuade _____

   (b) irrelevant _____

   (c) forbid _____

   (d) lead _____

Word Worm Anagram

3. Choose every third letter and then rearrange them to make a list word.

Difficult words I have found	Practise	Practise

Unit 29

4. Use list and revision words to solve the crossword.

Across

1. Uneven.
4. Faith.
5. The answer to a problem.
6. Harmony.
7. Allow.
8. It lets the light in.
9. Relevant.
11. Conversion.
13. Hue.

Down

1. Unsuitable.
2. Pills.
3. Her husband has died.
7. Convince.   9. Sweat.   10. Go after.   12. An archer uses it.

Missing Words

5. Use list or revision words to complete these sentences.

(a) Can you _____ that little boy to take his

_____?

(b) It is my _____ that the _____ is inaccurate.

(c) What _____ of curtains should we put at that

_____?

Change the Tense

6. Complete these list words.

(a)	persist	persists	persisted
(b)	follow		
(c)	persuade		
(d)	colour		

List Words	Practise	Practise	D
quit			
require			
queue			
equip			
mascara			
scarce			
discard			
scarlet			
million			
thousand			

All Mixed Up

1. Unjumble these list words.

   (a) pique   _____

   (b) qeerriu   _____

   (c) rascelt   _____

   (d) cridsad   _____

Revision Words	
easy	achieve
impatient	irrational
politician	distribution

Adding Endings

2. Add 'ment' or 'ly' to make a new word.

   (a) scarce   _____

   (b) require   _____

   (c) impatient _____

   (d) equip   _____

   (e) achieve   _____

Mirror Writing

3. Write the mirror written words correctly.

   (a) require   _____

   (b) mascara   _____

   (c) scarlet   _____

   (d) queue   _____

   (e) scarce   _____

Difficult words I have found	Practise	Practise

4. Use list and revision words to solve the wordsearch.

m	a	s	c	a	r	a	r	e	w	q	q	q
t	n	c	a	c	h	i	e	v	e	x	u	u
y	n	o	i	l	l	i	m	t	a	c	i	e
p	v	x	i	r	p	t	h	d	s	v	t	u
u	o	z	e	t	i	o	i	i	y	t	n	e
i	b	l	w	o	u	j	u	s	y	e	e	r
o	n	a	i	s	q	b	y	c	u	l	i	i
p	m	s	a	t	e	k	i	a	i	r	t	u
l	m	n	q	p	i	l	t	r	o	a	a	q
k	d	d	q	w	e	c	r	d	t	c	p	e
j	n	f	g	h	j	k	i	l	p	s	m	r
h	b	l	a	n	o	i	t	a	r	r	i	z
s	c	a	r	c	e	g	f	d	n	s	a	d

quit
queue
equip
require
million
easy
impatient
politician

mascara
discard
scarce
scarlet
thousand
achieve
irrational
distribution

Memory Master

5. (a) Cover the list and revision words. Write four from memory.

_____ _____

_____ _____

(b) For each word, write a question that has the word as its answer.

(i) _____

(ii) _____

(iii) _____

(iv) _____

Mixed Up Sentences

6. Unjumble the sentences and write them below.

(a) will distribution a the The thousand leaflets. publicity of require

_____

(b) to politician. to impatient a achieve was his ambition He be

_____

(c) wore and blue lady lipstick The mascara. scarlet

_____

(d) quit but smoking trying she not it is to easy. mum is finding My

_____

List Words	Practise	Practise	D
quality			
qualification			
quay			
quake			
unique			
clique			
antique			
picturesque			
monitor			
modem			

Alphabetical Order

1. Put the words beginning with 'qu' in alphabetical order.

   _____

   _____

   _____

   _____

Synonyms

2. Find a list word with a similar meaning.

   (a) scenic   _____

   (b) tremor   _____

   (c) screen   _____

   (d) incomparable   _____

   (e) wharf   _____

   (f) exclusive   _____

Missing Letters

3. Complete the list word.

   (a) __ __ a __ i __ i __ a __ i __ __

   (b) __ __ a __ __

   (c) __ __ __ __ i __ __ r

   (d) __ __ a __

   (e) __ __ t i __ __ __

Revision Words

stationery	noisy
inaccurate	illiterate
irresponsible	discretion

Difficult words I have found	Practise	Practise

4. Use list and revision words to solve the crossword.

Across

5. Scenic.

8. You may have this when you finish your studies.

10. Unable to read and write.

12. Loud.

13. Wharf.

14. Reckless.

15. A computer connector.

Down

1. Supervise.

2. In-group.

3. Writing paper and envelopes.

4. Tact.

6. The only one is.

7. Incorrect.

8. Worth.

9. Very old.

11. Tremble.

Secret Words

5. (a) Change 'qu' to 'aw' in quay.

_____

(b) Change the second 'm' to 'rn' in modem.

_____

(c) Change 'uni' to 'mos' in unique.

_____

(d) Change 'ke' to 'il' in quake.

_____

Extend Yourself

6. This word can be used as a noun or an adjective. Write a sentence for each.

monitor

(a) _____

(b) _____

List Words	Practise	Practise	D
consignment			
resign			
signature			
assignment			
benevolent			
benefactor			
beneficial			
beneficiary			
garden			
balloon			

Rhyming Words

1. Write a list word that rhymes.

   (a) artificial   _____

   (b) design   _____

   (c) soon   _____

   (d) malevolent   _____

   (e) pardon   _____

Letters into Words

2. Write three list words using the letters on the balloon.

   r e u s g d a i t n m

   _____

   _____

   _____

Revision Words

nation	tidy
science	immature
irresistible	deletion

Incorrect Words

3. (a) resine   _____

   (b) benefisiary   _____

   (c) benevolant   _____

   (d) asignment   _____

   (e) gardin   _____

Difficult words I have found	Practise	Practise

Unit 32

4. Use list and revision words to solve the wordsearch.

consignment   beneficial

resign   benevolent

signature   benefactor

assignment   beneficiary

garden   balloon

nation   tidy

science   immature

irresistible   deletion

a	s	s	i	g	n	m	e	n	t	q	w	i
s	l	k	j	h	a	g	e	c	f	d	r	m
i	y	d	i	t	t	x	c	o	z	r	s	m
g	r	r	g	k	i	i	n	n	e	d	t	a
n	o	c	a	j	o	p	e	s	b	e	n	t
a	t	v	r	i	n	o	i	i	a	l	e	u
t	c	b	d	h	c	s	c	g	l	e	l	r
u	a	n	e	g	t	i	s	n	l	t	o	e
r	f	m	n	i	u	i	f	m	o	i	v	e
e	e	m	b	f	d	s	a	e	o	o	e	r
p	n	l	r	e	s	i	g	n	n	n	n	t
o	e	n	b	v	c	x	z	t	a	e	e	y
i	b	l	a	i	c	i	f	e	n	e	b	u

Base Words

5. Write the base words for each of these words

(a) consignment _____   (b) signature _____

(c) irresistible _____   (d) assignment _____

(e) deletion _____   (f) immature _____

(g) beneficial _____   (h) scientific _____

(i) national _____

(j) gardener _____

My Meanings

6. Write a definition for each of the list and revision words below. Use a dictionary to check your answers.

(a) benevolent _____

(b) immature _____

(c) resign _____

(d) consignment _____

(e) signature _____

(f) benefactor _____

(g) science _____

(h) assignment _____

Revision Unit 5

List Words	Practise	Practise	D
eighty			
million			
balloon			
monitor			
seventy			
colour			
modem			
thousand			
leave			
ninety			

All Mixed Up

1. Unjumble these revision words.

   (a) houndsat   _____   (b) evela   _____

   (c) roomtin   _____   (d) linmoli   _____

   (e) tenyin   _____   (f) hygite   _____

Missing Words

2. Complete using the revision words.

   (a) _____ and _____ is one hundred and seventy.

   (b) A full size hot air _____ costs at least a _____ pounds.

   (c) Can you _____ how well that _____ is working?

   (d) _____ that wall cream and put a contrasting

   _____ on that wall.

Shape Sorter

3. Write a revision word that fits in each shape.

   (a) 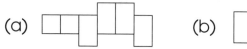   (b)

   (c) 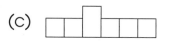   (d)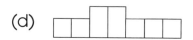

4. Find 12 mistakes and write them correctly on the lines.

Sefenty milion people will monetor the progress the hot air ballon

_____

using a moden on their computers. Eigty to ninty thusand spectators

_____

will release small ballons of every color as they watch it leve.

_____

Word Hunt

5. (a) Find three words which can be verbs or nouns.

_____ _____

_____

(b) Which word has a double consonant and a double vowel?

_____

(c) Which word names a number smaller than a million, but larger than a hundred?

_____

(d) Which two words are computer words?

_____

_____

Alphabetical Order

6. Write all the revision words in alphabetical order.

_____

_____

_____

Mixed Up Sentences

7. Unjumble the sentences and write them below.

(a) balloon The beautiful colour. a blue was

_____

(b) million match people Over football worldwide. watched the eighty

_____

(c) to leave One the their thousand because hurricane. of homes had people

_____

My Dictionary Words: Aa to Ii _____

Aa	Bb	Cc
Dd	Ee	Ff
Gg	Hh	Ii

Jj

Kk

Ll

Mn

Nn

Oo

Pp

Qq

Rr

My Dictionary Words: S s to Z z _____

Ss

Tt

Uu

Vv

Ww

Xx

Yy

Zz